NARWHAL

UNICORN OF THE SEA

BEN CLANTON

EGMONT

FOR ENYA
A.K.A. NUNU, A.K.A. JELLYFISH-FLINGER, A.K.A. MERMICORN

EGMONT
We bring stories to life

FIRST PUBLISHED IN CANADA 2016 BY TUNDRA BOOKS
FIRST PUBLISHED IN GREAT BRITAIN 2019
BY EGMONT UK LIMITED
2 MINSTER COURT, LONDON EC3R 7BB
PUBLISHED BY ARRANGEMENT WITH TUNDRA BOOKS,
AN IMPRINT OF PENGUIN RANDOM HOUSE CANADA YOUNG READERS,
A PENGUIN RANDOM HOUSE COMPANY

TEXT AND ILLUSTRATIONS COPYRIGHT © 2016 BEN CLANTON

ISBN 978 1 4052 9530 7

A CIP CATALOGUE RECORD FOR THIS TITLE IS AVAILABLE FROM THE BRITISH LIBRARY

70607/006

PRINTED IN ITALY

CONTENTS

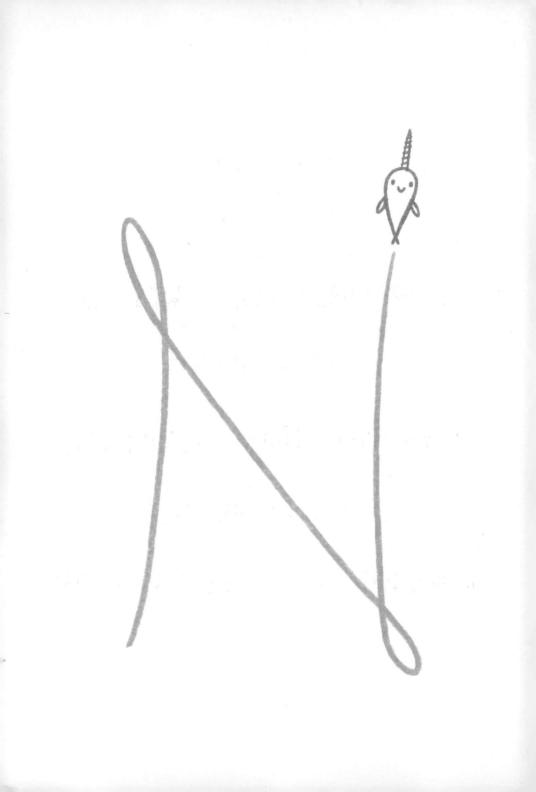

NARWHAL IS REALLY AWESOME

ONE DAY WHEN NARWHAL WAS OUT FOR A SWIM, HE FOUND HIMSELF IN NEW WATERS.

WHOA! *WHAT* ARE YOU?!

ME? I'M NARWHAL THE NARWHAL!

A NARWHAL?

YEP! UNICORN OF THE SEA!

YOU'VE NEVER HEARD OF A JELLYFISH?!

NOPE! YOU DON'T LOOK LIKE ANY FISH I'VE EVER SEEN, BUT YOU DO LOOK KIND OF JELLY-ISH. I SURE HAVE AN AMAZING IMAGINATION.

I CAN'T BELIEVE THIS!
THE THING I'M IMAGINING
IS IMAGINING THAT IT
IS IMAGINING ME.

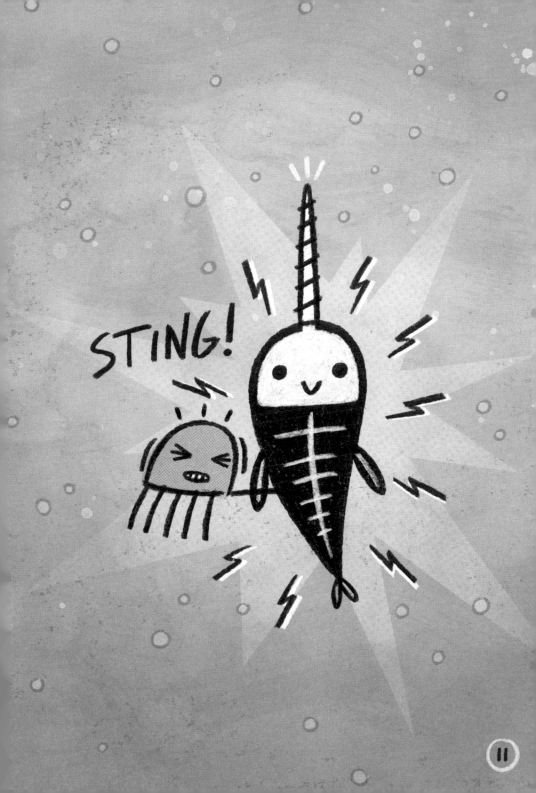

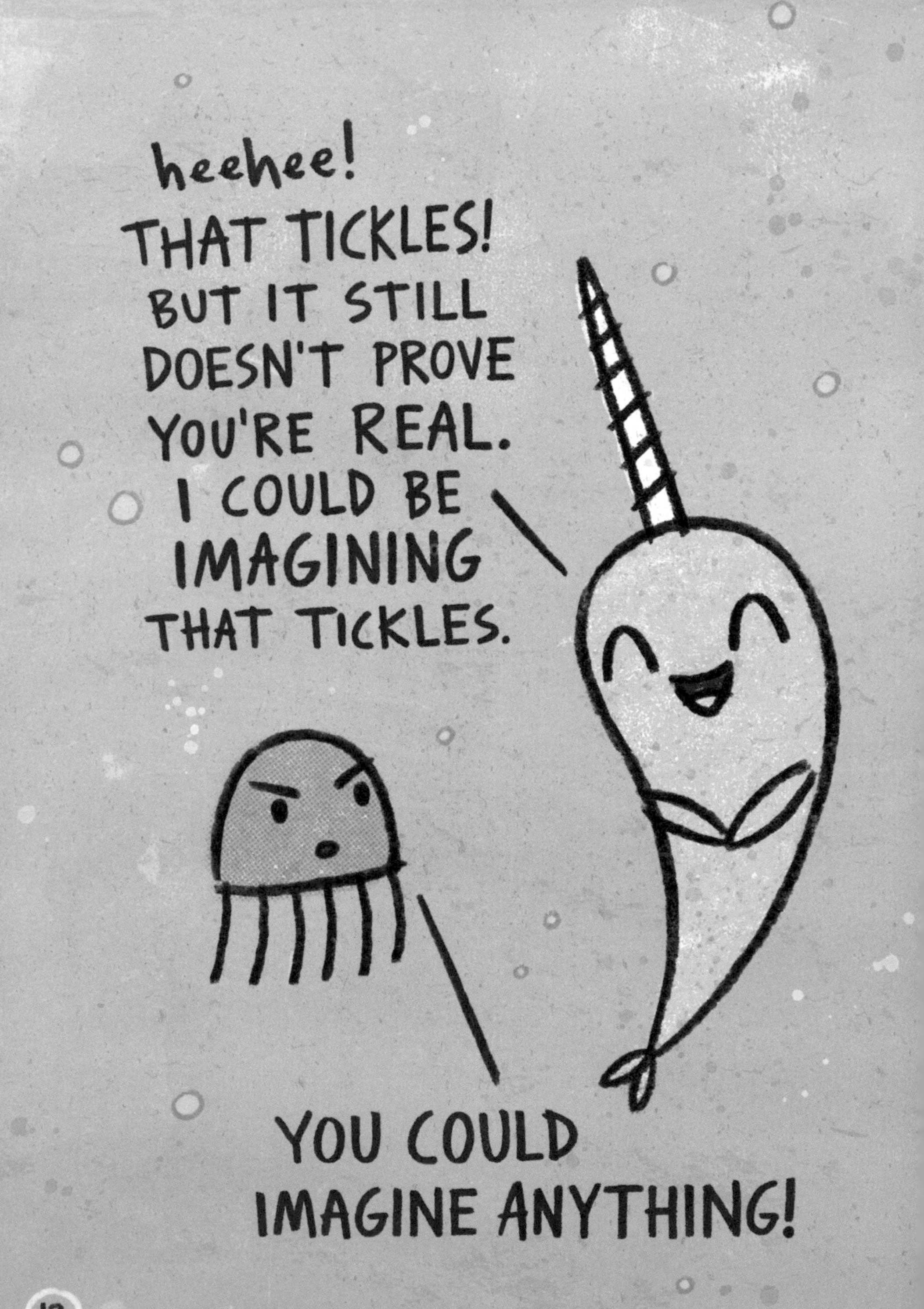
heehee!
THAT TICKLES! BUT IT STILL DOESN'T PROVE YOU'RE REAL. I COULD BE IMAGINING THAT TICKLES.
YOU COULD IMAGINE ANYTHING!

13

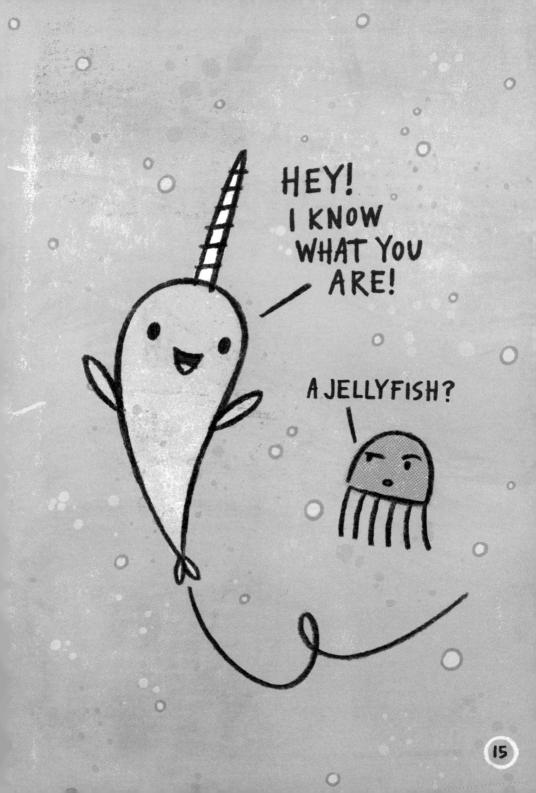

AN IMAGINARY FRIEND!!!

SURE THING!
COOL!
WELL, YOU MIGHT NOT BE REAL... BUT...
I THINK YOU'LL BE A REALLY GOOD FRIEND.

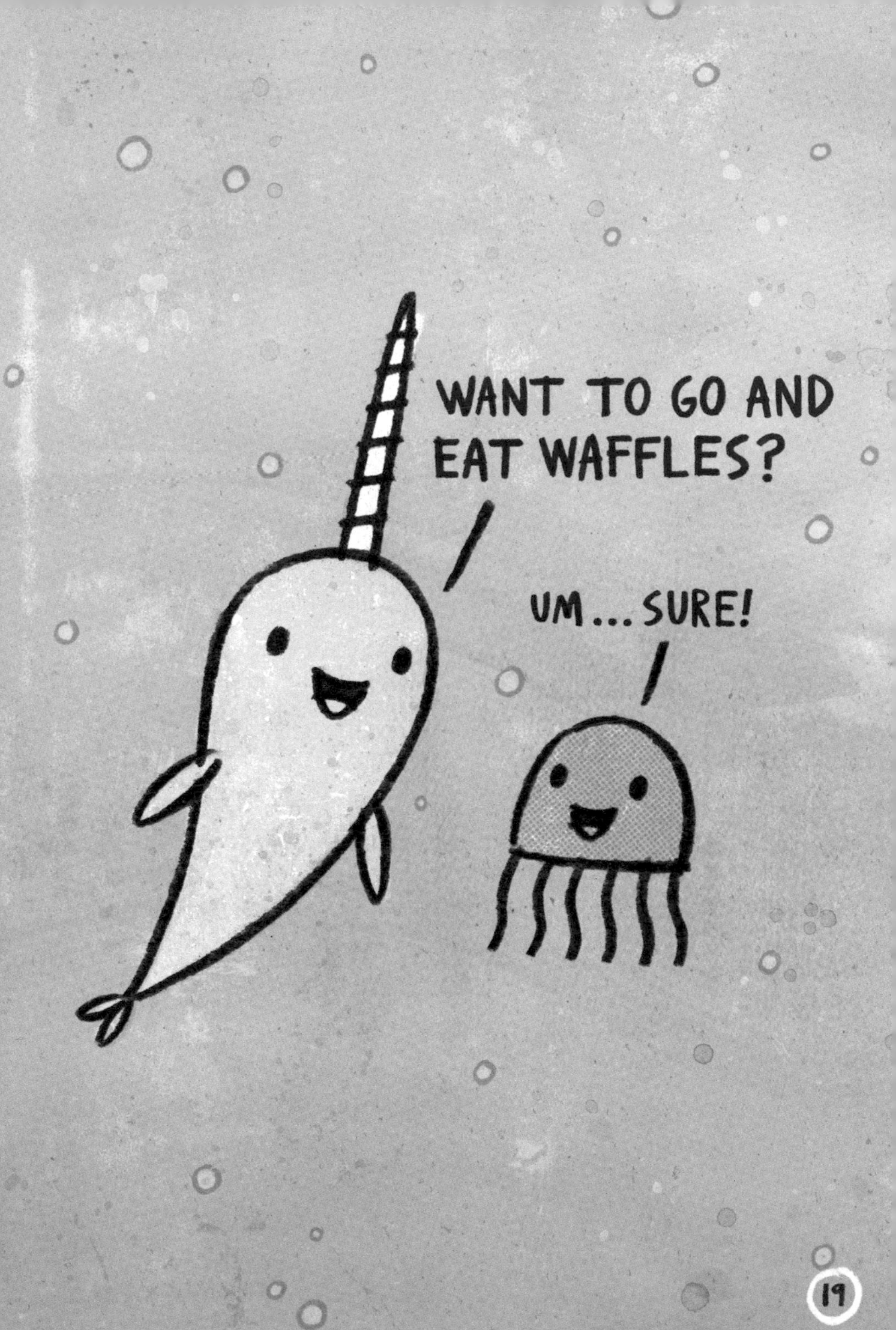
WANT TO GO AND EAT WAFFLES?
UM... SURE!

REALLY FUN FACTS

A NARWHAL'S LONG, HORN-LIKE TOOTH CAN REACH UP TO 3 m (10 ft) LONG!

I BRUSH EVERY DAY!

WOW!

I'M AMAZING!

NARWHALS CAN WEIGH 1,600 kg (3,500 lb) AND HOLD THEIR BREATH FOR 25 min.

THE RECORD DIVE DEPTH FOR A NARWHAL IS 1,800 m (5,905 ft, OVER ONE MILE).

RECENT RESEARCH SUGGESTS NARWHALS CAN LIVE UP TO 90 YEARS.

MORE REALLY FUN FACTS

THERE ARE NEARLY 4,000 TYPES OF JELLYFISH IN THE WORLD.

WHOA!!! I WONDER WHAT KIND I AM...

THE AWESOME KIND!

NOT TO BE CONFUSED WITH A SNACK.

A GROUP OF JELLYFISH IS CALLED A SMACK.

JELLYFISH HAVE BEEN AROUND FOR MILLIONS OF YEARS. WELL BEFORE DINOSAURS!

THE STING FROM SOME JELLYFISH CAN BE DEADLY FOR HUMANS.

THE DEADLY ONES ARE FOUND MAINLY IN AUSTRALIA.

NARWHAL'S POD OF AWESOMENESS

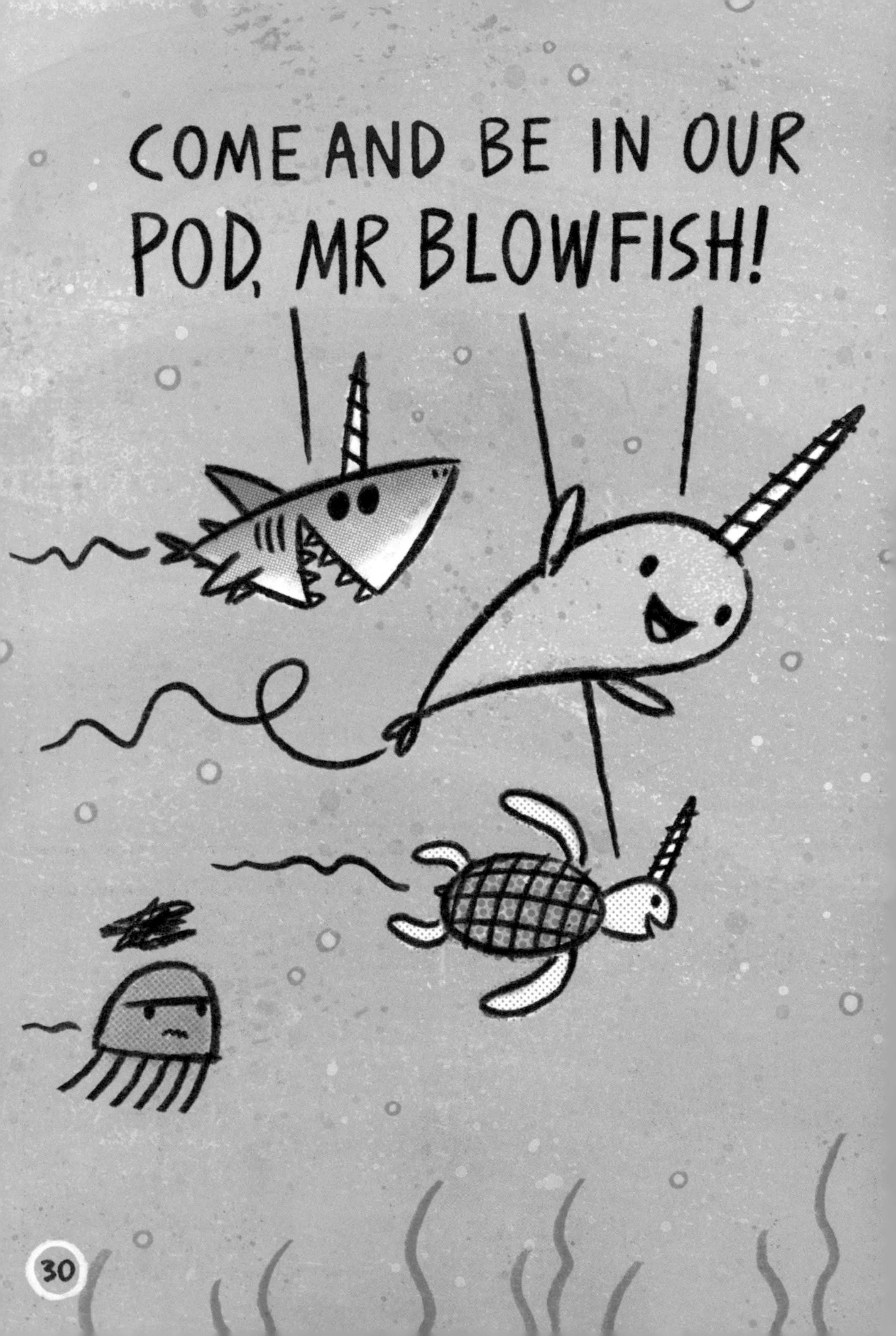
COME AND BE IN OUR POD, MR BLOWFISH!

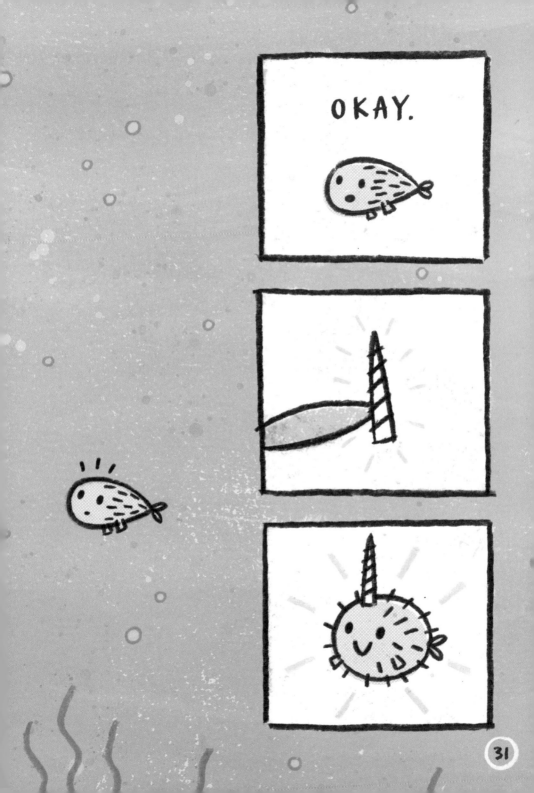

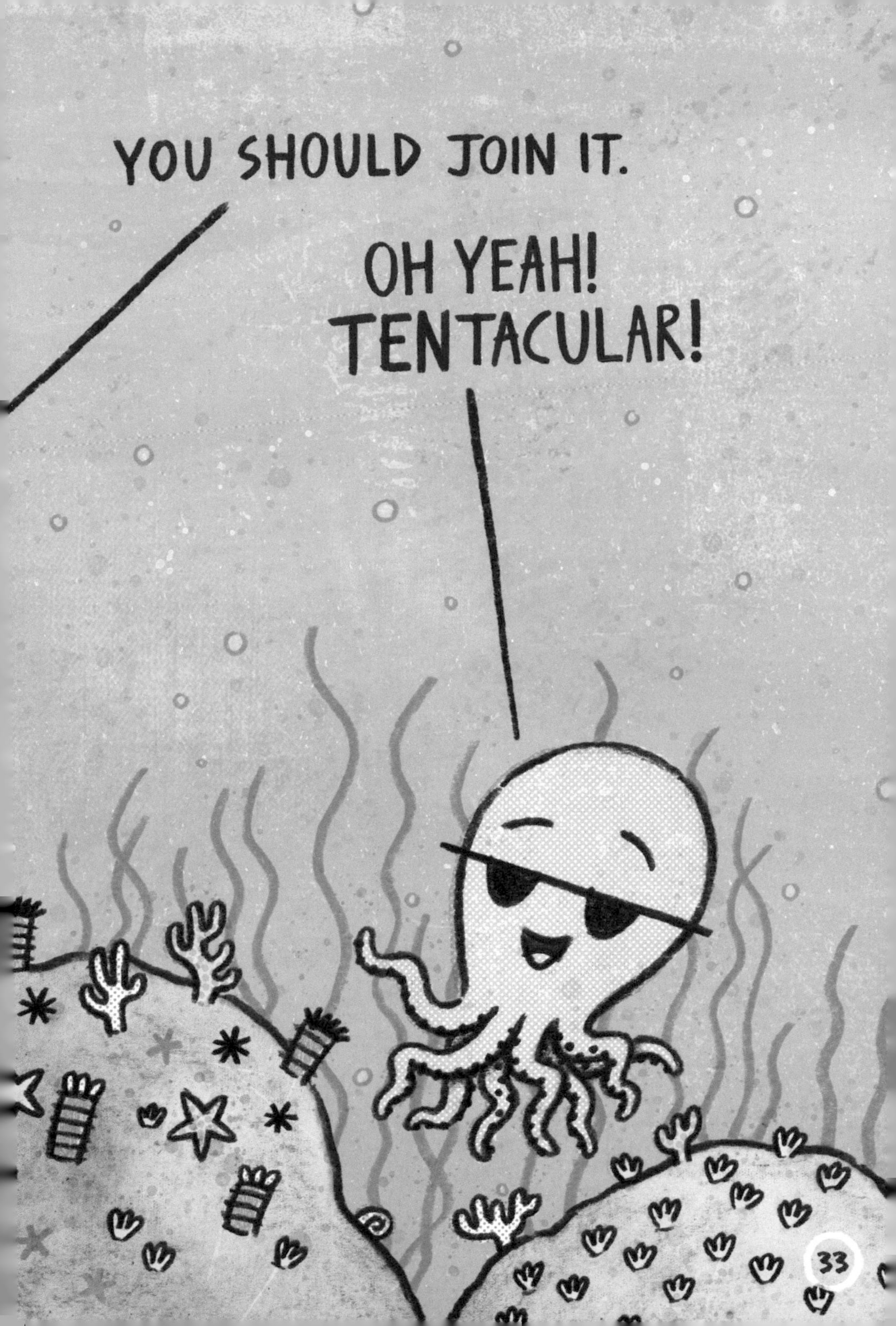
YOU SHOULD JOIN IT.
OH YEAH! TENTACULAR!

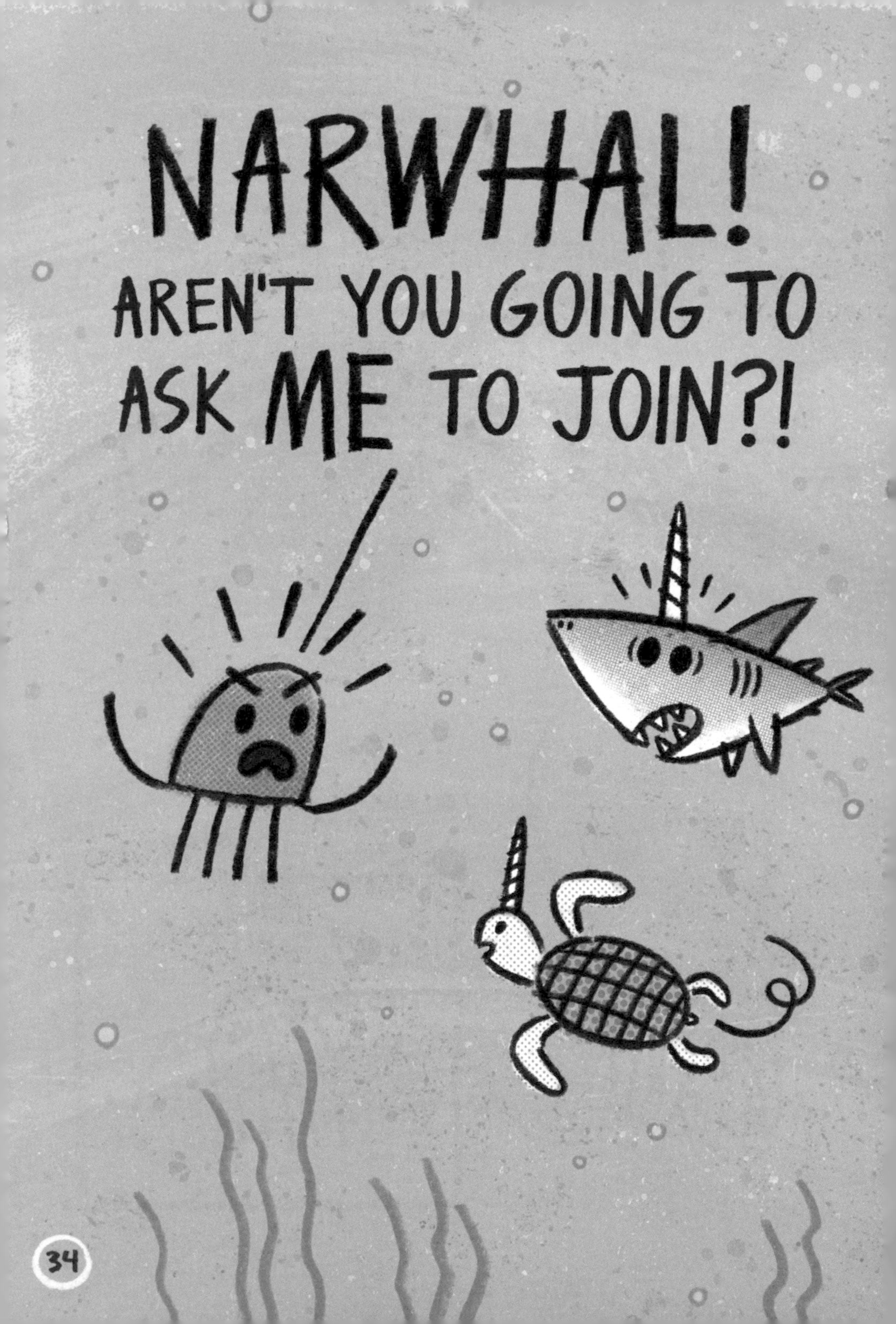
NARWHAL!
AREN'T YOU GOING TO ASK ME TO JOIN?!

OH! I DIDN'T ASK?
I GUESS I THOUGHT
WE WERE MAKING
THE POD TOGETHER.
YOU DO WANT TO BE
PART OF OUR POD,
RIGHT, JELLY?

UM...WELL...

I'M NOT REALLY SURE!

BUT I IMAGINE A POD PLAYS
ULTIMATE CANNONBALL, EATS
WAFFLES, FIGHTS CRIME AND...

HAS SUPER AWESOME PARTIES!

I DO LOVE PARTIES!

NAR WHAL!

NARWHAL
AND THE
BEST
BOOK
EVER!

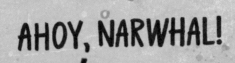

YUM! WAFFLE!

51

GOOD THING THAT WAFFLE
IS A KUNG FU MASTER!

LOOK AT THE BOOK AND SEE
A PICTURE OF IT BATTLING
THE ROBOT!

I'VE GOT AN IDEA!
THE WAFFLE SHOULD
HAVE A SIDEKICK! A
STRAWBERRY!

NICE ONE, JELLY!

I GET IT, NARWHAL!
THIS BOOK IS THE BEST!
IT CAN BE ABOUT ANYTHING
YOU WANT IT TO BE ABOUT!

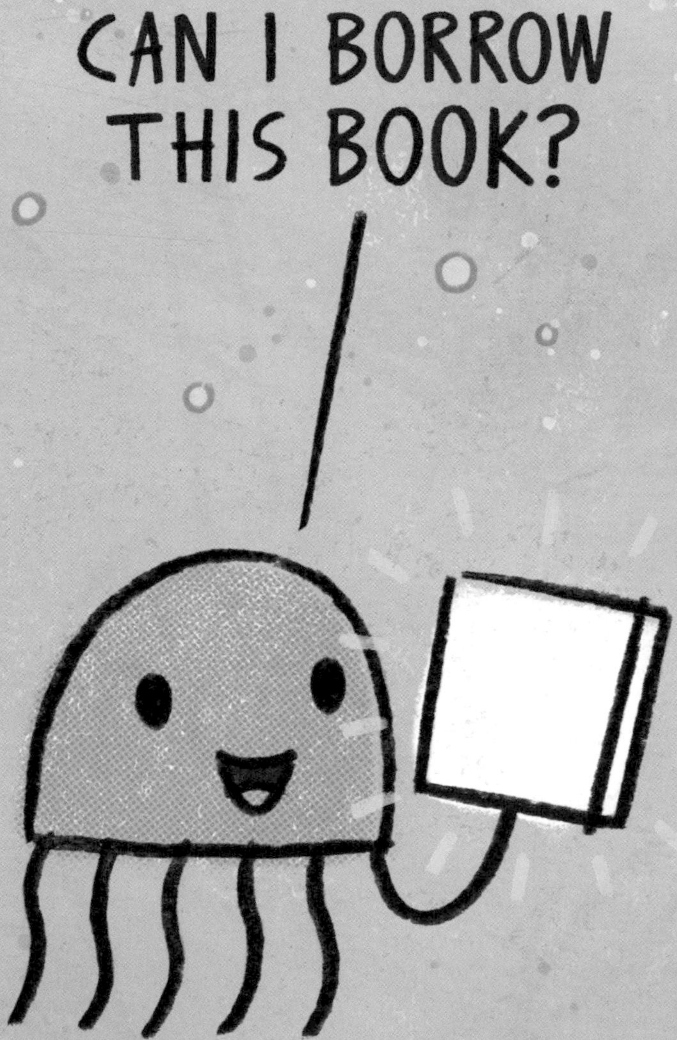
CAN I BORROW THIS BOOK?

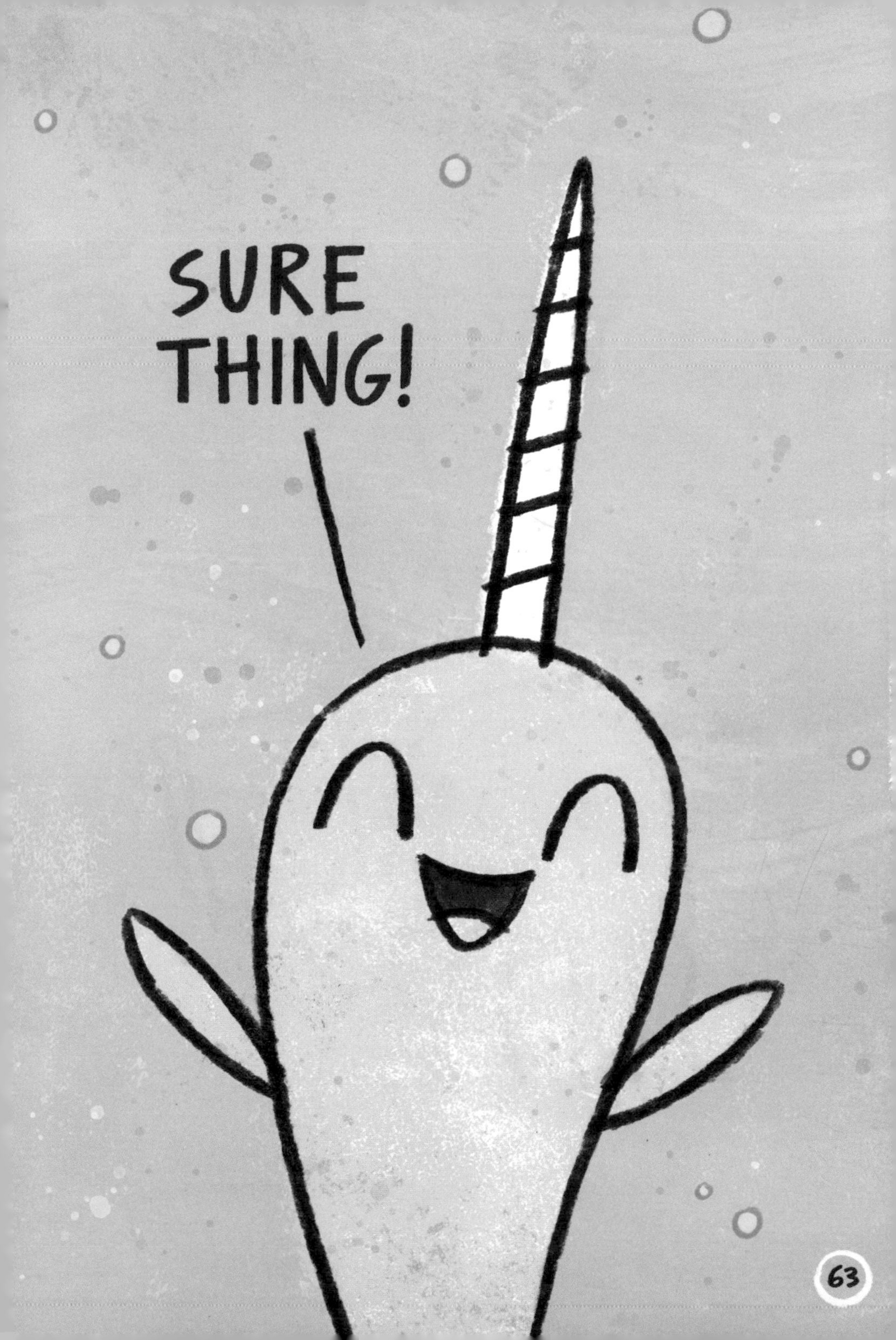
SURE THING!